TRINITY
COLLEGE LONDON PRESS

CW00434988

GRADE **02**

SINGING

Songs & Teaching Notes for
Trinity College London
Exams 2018–2021

Includes CD of
piano accompaniments
and pronunciation guides

Published by
Trinity College London Press
trinitycollege.com

Registered in England
Company no. 09726123

Copyright © 2017 Trinity College London Press
First impression, September 2017

Printed in England by Caligraving Ltd.

Farewell, Lad

Trad. Catalan
Arrangement and English lyrics by
Jackie O'Neill

Fare-well, lad, a fond fare-well, lad. I weep and grieve at the thought of

part - ing. Fare - well, lad, a fond fare - well, and I pray one

hand - some, be-comes a sol - dier in days of war. Re-

-turn when the fight-ing's o'er when your cap-tain brave needs you there no more._____

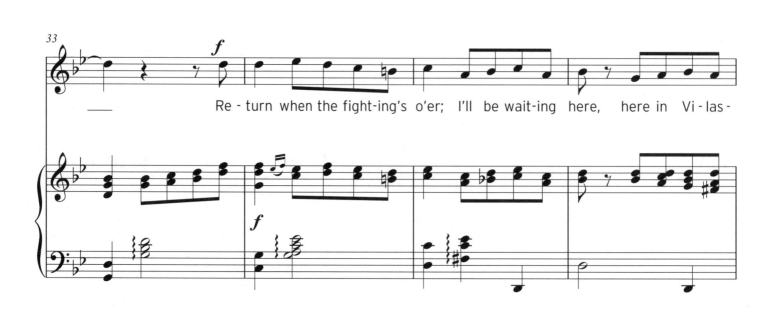

____ Re - turn when the fight-ing's o'er; I'll be wait-ing here, here in Vi - las -

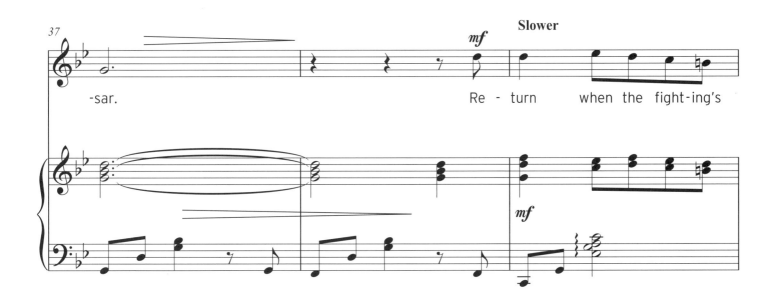

-sar.

Re - turn   when   the   fight-ing's

o'er;   I'll   be   wait-ing   here,   here   in   Vi - las - sar.

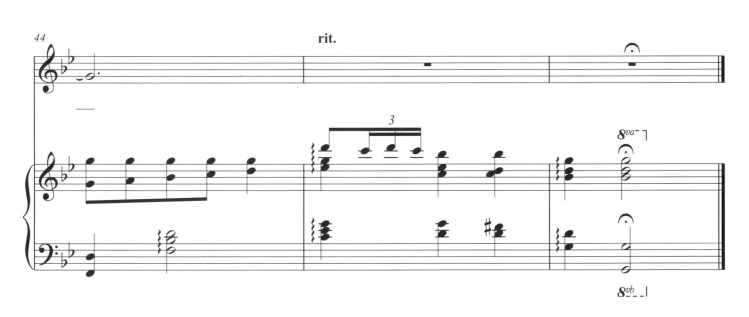

Westering Home

Words and music by
Hugh S Roberton
(1874–1952)

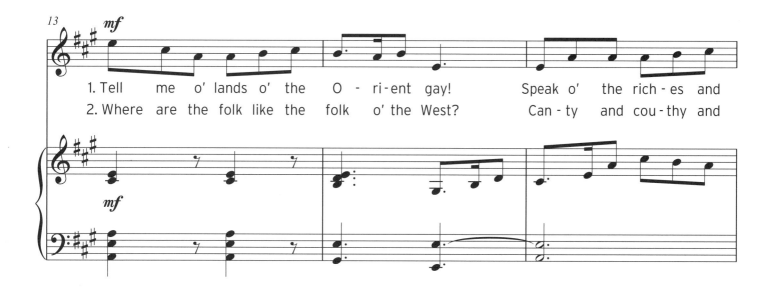

1. Tell me o' lands o' the O-ri-ent gay! Speak o' the rich-es and
2. Where are the folk like the folk o' the West? Can-ty and cou-thy and

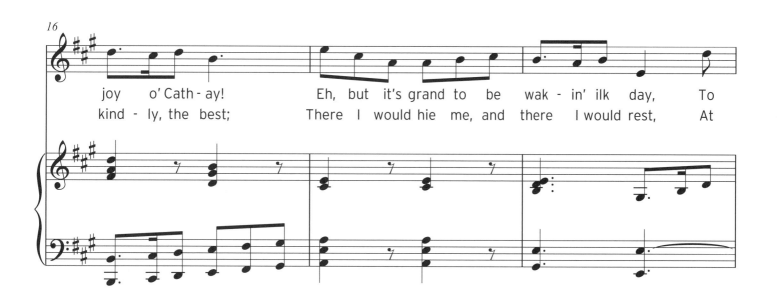

joy o' Cath-ay! Eh, but it's grand to be wak-in' ilk day, To
kind-ly, the best; There I would hie me, and there I would rest, At

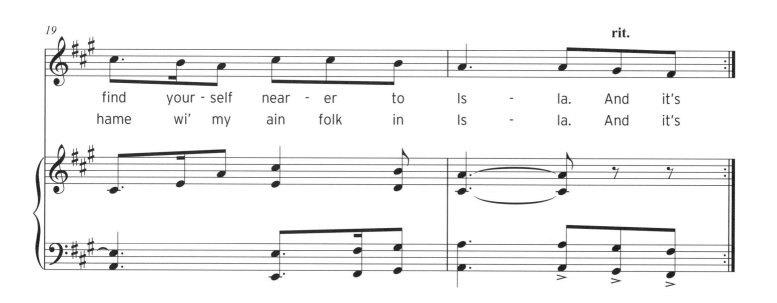

find your-self near-er to Is - la. And it's
hame wi' my ain folk in Is - la. And it's

West-er-ing home, and a song in the air, Light in the eye, and it's

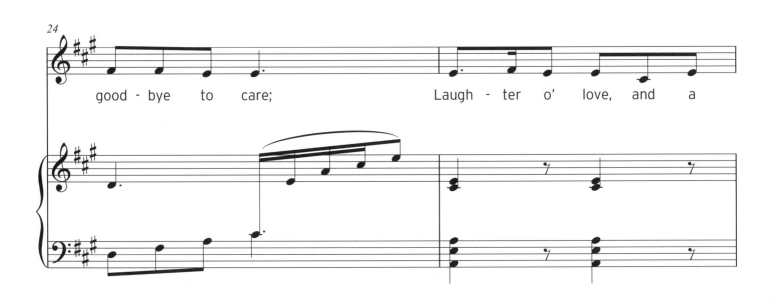

good - bye to care; Laugh-ter o' love, and a

wel-com-ing there; Isle of my heart, my own one!

Evening in Autumn

Anon.

William Henry Anderson
(1882-1955)

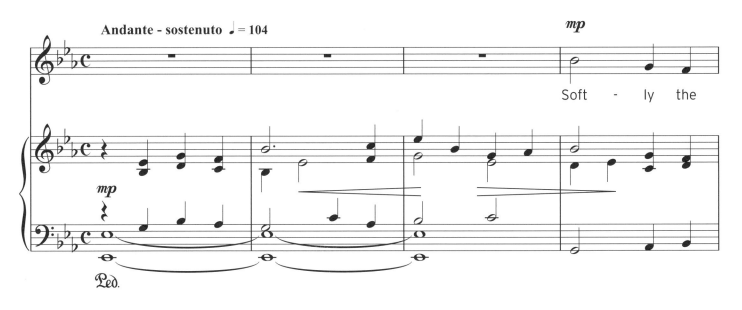

Soft - ly the

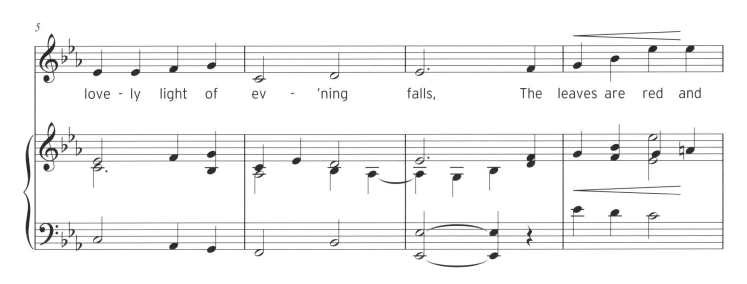

love - ly light of ev - 'ning falls, The leaves are red and

glow a-gainst the sky,____ Up - on the hill_____ the

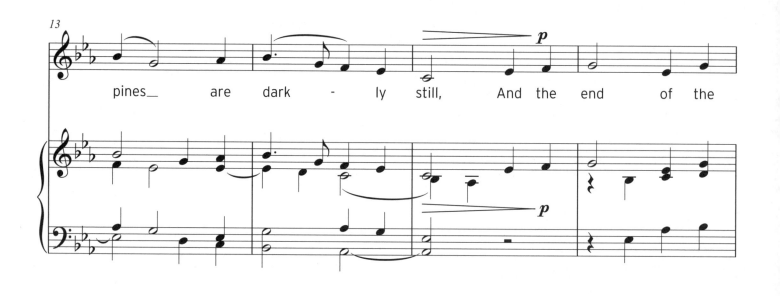

pines___ are dark - ly still, And the end of the

day steals slow - ly by._____

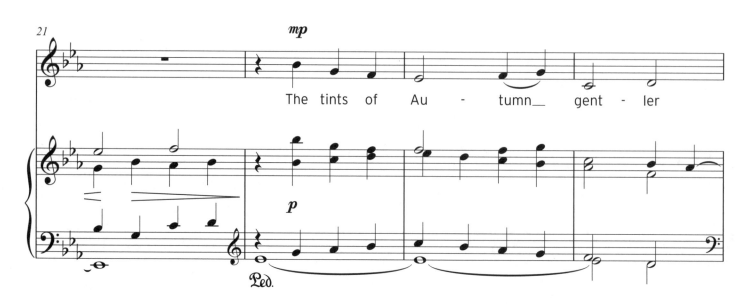

The tints of Au - tumn___ gent - ler

seem Af - ter the parch -ing heat of wind__ and sun.__

There is a mel - low-ing of all which brings a qui - et-ness of

soul When day____ when day__ is__ done.____

for the Purley and District Schools Music Association

The Spanish Main

R V Knox

Arthur Baynon
(1889-1954)

I've asked a great ma - ny

peo - ple. But no - bo - dy seems to know, How the pi - rates kept_ their

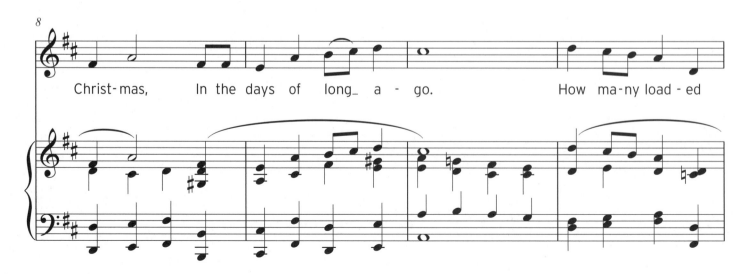

Christ - mas, In the days of long_ a - go. How ma - ny load - ed

gal - leons On Christ - mas_ day they sank, And_ how ma-ny mer - chant

sea - men They_ made to walk the plank.

Or wheth - er they chant - ed car - ols As

round the_ docks they rolled And made each o - ther pre - sents, Out

of their hoard of gold, And cov-ered a mast with green leaves, And
called it a Christ-mas tree And hung it with shin-ing se - quins On the
shore of a tro-pi-cal sea. And
lit the rum round the pud - ding And cursed in a friend - ly

way But re-fused to do a-ny busi-ness Be - cause it was Christ-mas

Day, I've asked a____great ma-ny peo-ple, But no - bo-dy seems to

allargando

know, How the pi - rates kept their Christ - mas In the days of

cresc - - - - - - en - - - - - do

long a - go.____

15

The Skylark

Marjorie E Kirtley

Eric Thiman
(1900-1975)

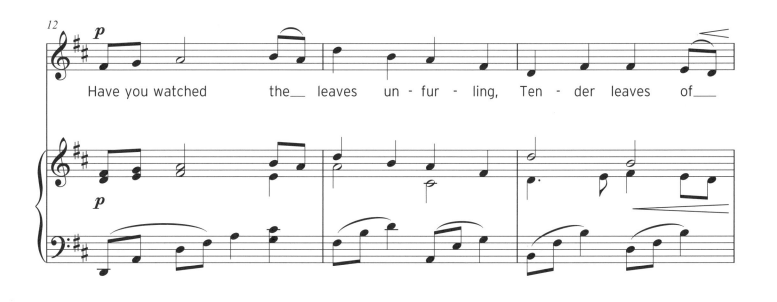

Have you watched the__ leaves un - fur - ling, Ten - der leaves of__

green?__ Ev - 'ry__ tree to beau - ty__ wa - king,

poco rall.

Love - ly, love - ly__ as a queen.

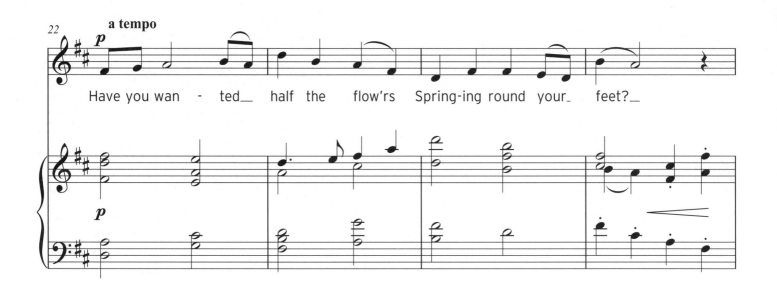

Have you wan - ted__ half the flow'rs Spring-ing round your__ feet?__

Each one__bring - ing God's good wish - es, You, his child, to__

greet.____

Ghosts in the Belfry

John O' The North

Havelock Nelson
(1917-1996)

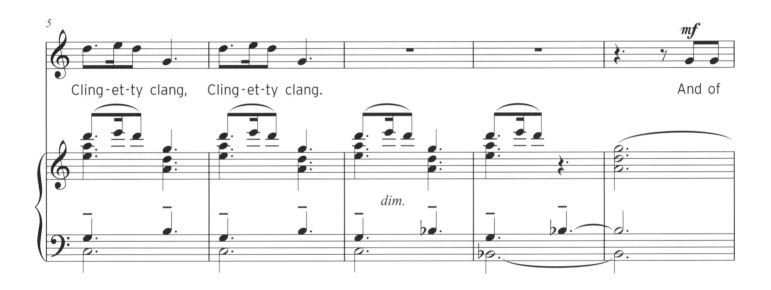

The sex - ton

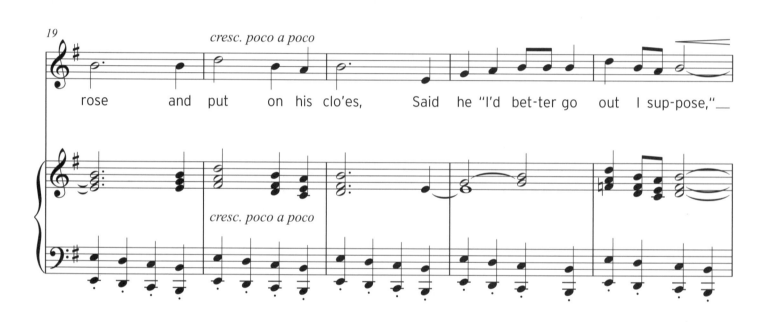

rose and put on his clo'es, Said he "I'd bet-ter go out I sup-pose,"

But when he got to the bel - fry stair

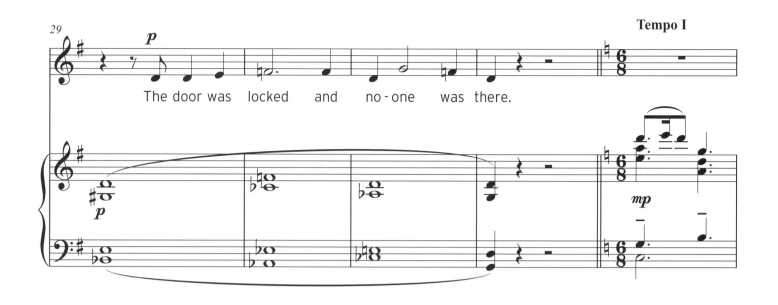

The door was locked and no-one was there.

Who was it then that rang the bell?

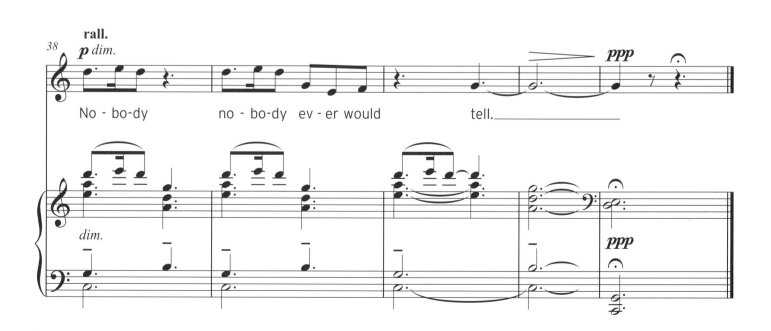

No-bo-dy no-bo-dy ev-er would tell.

The World's End

Eleanor Farjeon

Mervyn Burtch
(1929–2015)

1. A coach-and-six to Chel - sea, A coach-and-six to Chel - sea, A

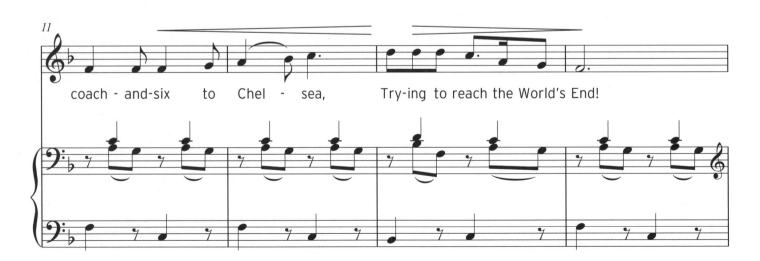

coach - and-six to Chel - sea, Try-ing to reach the World's End!

Omit verse 3 in the exam.

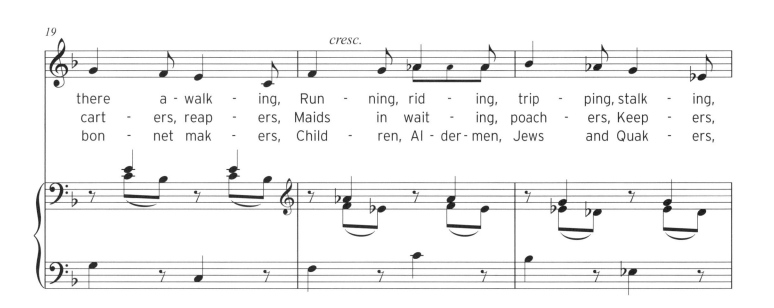

*Omit verse 3 in the exam.

End.
End.
End.

coach - and-six to Chel - sea, A coach - and-six to Chel - sea, A

coach - and - six to Chel - sea, Try - ing to reach the World's

End!

Abdul, the Magician

Words and music by
Clifford Crawley
(1929-2016)

1. Ab - dul the ma - gic - ian_____ is us - ual - ly dressed in black, He
2. Ab - dul the ma - gic - ian_____ has an - i - mals by the score, He

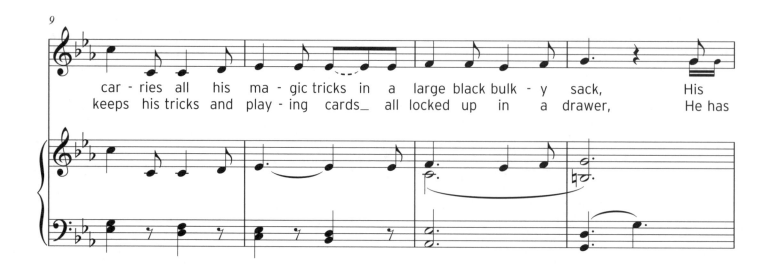

car - ries all his ma - gic tricks in a large black bulk - y sack, His
keeps his tricks and play - ing cards_ all locked up in a drawer, He has

Was he born with ma-gic powers, Or just the power to see that

if you're quick, have sleight of hand, you soon can fool_____ peo-ple like

me? you, and you, and

you, and you, and me?

Grizelda

Words and music by
Clifford Crawley
(1929-2016)

Adagio ♩ = 84   accel.   *mf*

mf

Griz-
Griz-

Allegro ♩ = 112

-el-da was a witch,   a witch she wished she was-n't, For she was as kind and gen-tle as could
-el-da was a witch,   a witch she wished she was-n't, But now she is hu-man just like you and

be.   She had a big black cat   and a
me.   She's bought a pure white cat   and she

f   *mf*

long and point - ed hat,   But she felt ve-ry much the same as you and me.   She
wears a feath-ered hat,   And she owns a new house a - cross the street from me.   I

tried to cast a spell,   a spell to make her hu - man   But she
hope that you are not   a - ny thing you wish you was - n't,   But

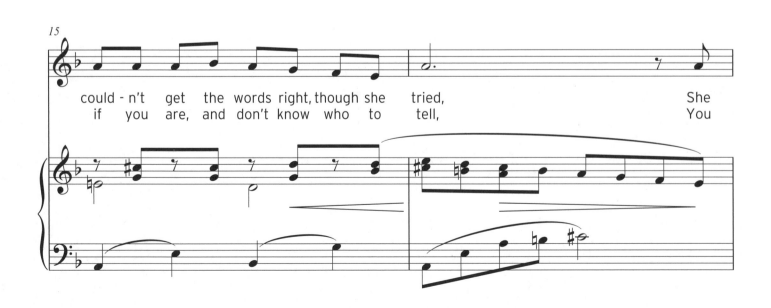

could - n't get the words right, though she tried,   She
if you are, and don't know who to tell,   You

A Fly

Ruth Dallas

Judith Exley
(b. 1939)

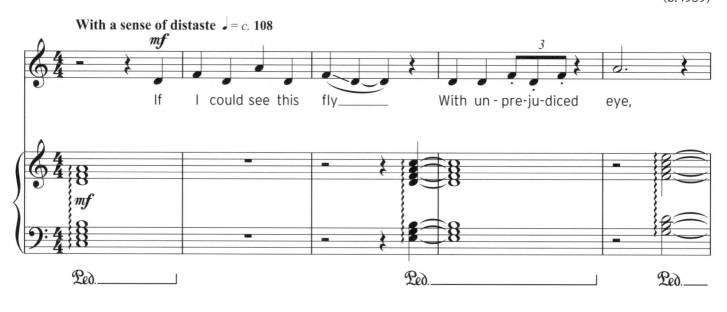

If I could see this fly_____ With un-pre-ju-diced eye,

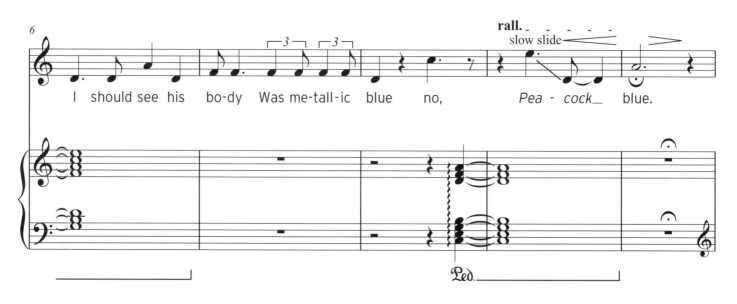

I should see his bo-dy Was me-tall-ic blue no, Pea-cock__ blue.

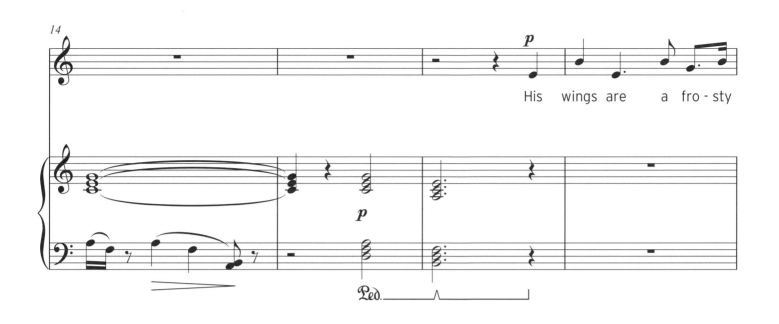

His wings are a fro-sty

puff; His legs fine wire. He e-ven has a face. I

no-tice And he breathes, as I do.

Pigs Could Fly

Words and music by
Howard Skempton
(b. 1947)

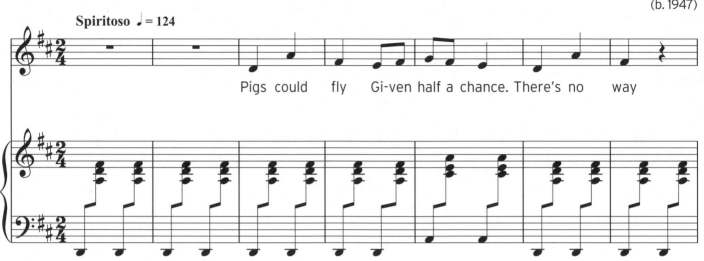

Has real_ flair. I would-n't pine For a po-lar bear. Or bill and coo With a

ca-ri-bou, Or fall off a log For a whale that sings. Give me a hog With wings, with

wings. La la la la la la la la, La la la la la la la,

La la la la la la la, La la la la la la la.

Commissioned by the York Region Board of Education, 1989

On the Back of an Eagle

Words and music by
Nancy Telfer
(b. 1950)

I would fly on the back of an ea - gle On a

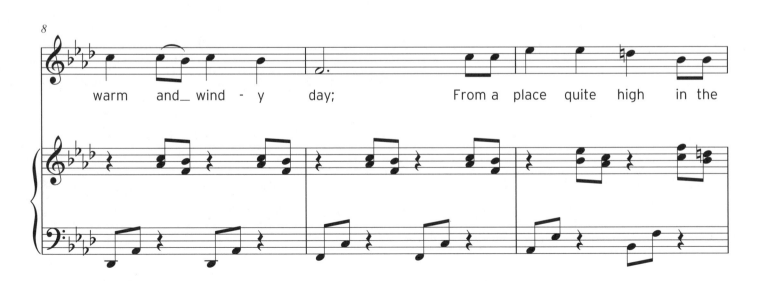

warm and_ wind - y day; From a place quite high in the

clear, blue sky, I would { feel the air blow-ing through my hair_____
look to see what is yet to be_____

And watch the___ sights be - low._____
And laugh with the spark - - ling sun._____

2nd time to Coda ⊕

f

Fly,_____ ea - gle;

fly_____ ea - gle; fly,_____ ea - gle, fly.

Love Me Sweet

Elizabeth Barret Browning
(1806-1861)

Carl Vine
(b. 1954)

Lyrics:

Love___ me sweet, with all your heart, Feel - ing, think - ing, see - ing;___

Love me with your light - est glance, Love me in full

Lyrics:
be - ing._____ Love me with your o - pen arms,

in their frank sur - ren - der;_____ With_____ the vow - ing

of your lips, in their si - lence ten - der._____

rall.

a tempo

*Omit bars 37 to 52 in the exam.

Love_____ me with your o - pen

arms, in_____ their frank sur - ren - der;_____

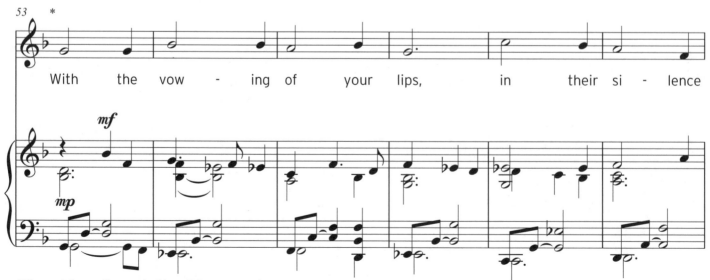

With the vow - ing of your lips, in their si - lence

*The cut from the end of bar 36 resumes here.

ten - der._____ Love me sweet, with all your heart,

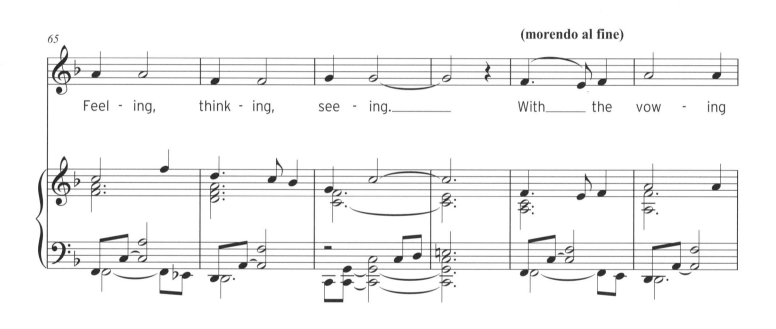

(morendo al fine)

Feel - ing, think - ing, see - ing._____ With_____ the vow - ing

rall. _ _ _ _

of your lips, in their si - lence ten - der._____

Rocking in Rhythm

Words and music by
Mira and Michael Coghlan
(b. 1955 / 1949)

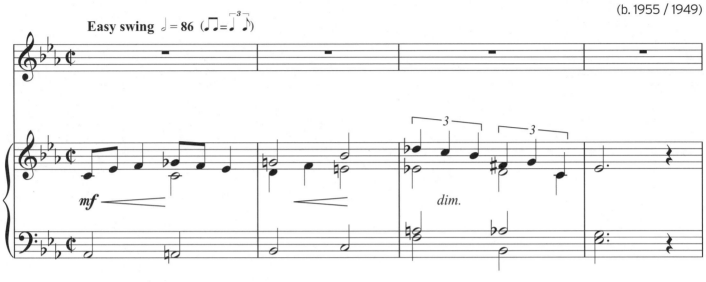

Rock - ing___ in rhy - thm___ roll - ing in rhyme
Laugh - ing___ and sing - ing___ rais - ing the roof

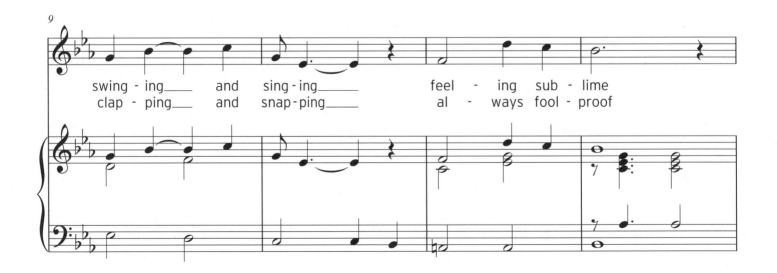

swing - ing___ and sing - ing___ feel - ing sub - lime
clap - ping___ and snap - ping___ al - ways fool - proof

D.S. al Coda

⊕ **Coda**

who could want an-y-thing more?

Reel-ing and rock-ing in

rhy - thm swing-ing and sing-ing and sway - ing reel-ing and rock-ing in

rhy - thm sing-ing swing-ing we're sing-ing and feel-ing just fine. Yeah

(whisper, very breathy)

Chocolate

from *Just Desserts*

Brian Moses

David Hamilton
(b. 1955)

My fa-vou-rite fla - vour is choc'-late whe-ther

ice - cream or cake. Mum al-ways says__ too much of it will

give me tum-my ache. I've tried just__ a -

-bout ev'-ry choc'-late__ bar_____ that shops_____

__ have e-ver sold. I don't_ think

I'd swap_ my choc - o - late_____ if you of - fered_ me

bars of___ gold.____

When

choc-o-late melts_ in my mouth   it's a hea - ven - ly taste.   I

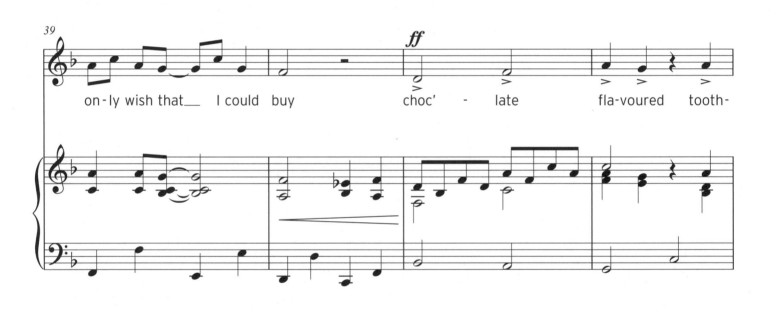

on-ly wish that__ I could buy   choc' - late   fla-voured   tooth-

- paste.

Teaching notes

Trad. *arr.* O'Neill   Farewell, Lad   page 2

Catalan is a language spoken primarily in certain areas of Spain, chiefly in the regions of Catalonia, Valencia and the Balearic Isles. Although it shares some similarities with Spanish, it is not a Spanish dialect but a distinct language in its own right, and has sounds that link it both to French and Italian. In this version, an English translation is used to make it accessible to a wider number of singers.

Although the mention of the Catalonian town of Vilassar at the end of the song reveals its geographical origins, the subject matter is universal as the singer bids farewell to a young man going to war. The simple but haunting melody of this song needs to be delivered with real feeling. The minor key sets up a mood of sorrow and you need to imagine waving goodbye to someone you may not see again. Try to think how you will vary the tone of your singing to communicate hope at the end of the piece as you tell the soldier that you will be waiting for him on his return. The final bars of the song are to be sung 'freely' and with the two pauses, you can really take your time here to help emphasise the fact that you will be waiting for him.

It is sometimes difficult to sing a sad song because when we are sad we lose energy and this can mean that our singing becomes flat and dull. So think how you can look and sound sad without losing a clear and rounded tone.

Roberton   Westering Home   page 6

Sir Hugh Stevenson Roberton was a Scottish conductor, composer and choral director who founded Glasgow's highly acclaimed Orpheus Choir. His mother is believed to have been a good singer who regularly sang many different folk songs to him as a child.

This song draws on that folk tradition, singing the praises of home above other places in the world. Home is Isla, which is the name of one of the islands off the coast of Scotland and the folk are 'canty' which means neat or trim and 'couthy' which means homely. The other unusual words in the song are 'ilk' which here means 'each' and 'hie' which means haste or hurry.

Keep the dotted rhythms really neat and accurate when you are singing to give a lovely sense of impetus to the song. This will help to convey the feeling of someone travelling homewards. There is one moment of ornamentation in the song, which also needs to be sung very cleanly. This is found on the word 'own' in the chorus and the name of the ornament is an *acciaccatura*. It is an extra note or grace note that is usually sung as quickly as possible before the note that follows. It is also sometimes called a crush or crushed note as the Italian word *acciaccatura* comes from the verb *acciaccare*, which means to crush.

Folk music often uses ornamentation or added notes to embellish a simple melody. Other styles of music use it too and singers sometimes add their own in a sort of improvisation. What can you find out about different ornaments and can you find some songs that use them?

Anderson   Evening in Autumn   page 9

William Henry Anderson was born in England and studied singing at the Guildhall School of Music. He sang in opera and as a lay tenor in London churches including St Paul's Cathedral. At the age of 28 he moved to Canada where he became a celebrated singing teacher. He was also a composer throughout his life, writing over 150 songs.

This song needs a lovely even tone and well-sustained lines. There are a number of dynamic markings to observe with some tricky *diminuendo* markings at ends of phrases. To help you with these, try practising single notes with both a steady *crescendo* and *diminuendo*, feeling how you need to control the breath pressure to achieve a good consistency of dynamic shape. The last phrase is marked *morendo* which means 'dying away' so make sure that you have enough air not only to sustain the last long note but also to achieve this effect. The two verses in this song are very similar but make sure you are singing the different

rhythms accurately. Listen too to how the piano part is different as, for example, at the opening to the second verse, where both hands play quite high. This adds a different colour to the song at this point.

Poets often use the changing seasons and times of day to suggest different moods. What mood do you think the words of this song are suggesting? Can you find other songs where either a particular time of year or a time of day is used to suggest a particular mood?

Baynon   The Spanish Main   page 12

Arthur Baynon was born in England in the late 19th century. He was a musical director and organist, gaining his Fellowship from the Royal College of Organists.

The 'galleons' mentioned in this song are sailing ships that were common on the seas between the 15th and 18th centuries so the pirates here really are from 'days of long ago'. Pirates of any bygone era are seen as bold and daring ruffians so this song needs to be sung with plenty of confident character though you do want your listeners to see all the 'pictures' of what the pirates might get up to on Christmas day so don't set off too fast. There are some big leaps to be negotiated with octaves, sixths and sevenths appearing in each verse. Make sure you pitch these very carefully and always open out the voice for the higher notes making sure you don't push the sound. The ending too is a challenge with a very long last note. It might be an idea to breathe before the last word 'ago' to give yourself plenty of air for sustaining the final note. Keep it very steady and without strain.

The traditions of Christmas in this song involve singing carols, giving presents and decorating a Christmas tree. Around the world though there are many different traditions associated with Christmas and with other major religious festivals. Can you find out more about different festivals and how people celebrate them?

Thiman   The Skylark   page 16

Eric Thiman, an English organist and composer, was largely self-taught but went on to achieve an FRCO and a MusD. He was a Professor of harmony at the Royal Academy of Music and the Dean of the Faculty of Music at London University.

This charming song is a celebration of the singing of the skylark and the coming of spring. The skylark is a small British bird, brown in colour and looking rather non-descript. However, it is famous for its display flights when it rises vertically up into the air, then hangs high over its territory singing a long and lively song that can be heard from quite a distance. It is particularly associated with the seasons of spring and early summer.

In order to convey the moods of this song, your singing needs to be very expressive with every detail of the dynamic contrasts observed. This is a good song to practise with an 'inner' smile. Try not to smile too much with your face as this can add tension into the jaw and constrict the sound but feel a sense of happiness inside and use your eyes to communicate this. As the accompaniment gets less busy in the final verse, don't let the forward momentum stop but keep the lines flowing forward until the final *allargando* where you can broaden and slow the tempo for two bars.

See if you can listen to a recording of a skylark singing. You might also like to listen to a piece of music by Vaughan Williams called *The Lark Ascending*. The composer based his music on a poem by George Meredith about the song of the skylark and in this piece, the violin is given the role of imitating the soaring song of the bird.

Havelock Nelson was a 20th-century composer and conductor. He studied at the Royal Irish Academy of Music and at Trinity College, Dublin, graduating with degrees in music and medical science. He was the staff accompanist for the BBC in Belfast for 30 years and later became the director of the Trinidad and Tobago opera company.

The setting for this song is a church belfry, which is the part of a tower that houses the church bell or bells. The sexton is the name of the person who looks after the church buildings and the churchyard. Part of the sexton's duties may also include ringing the church bell. So, in this song when the sexton hears the bell ringing he knows that there is something not right as not only is it late at night but it is not him ringing the bell.

In the first half of the song, notice how high the right hand of the piano is playing and this is clearly imitating the sound of the bell. You also imitate the sound when you sing 'clingetty clang' so although you are singing loudly at this point, keep the sound very resonant and bell-like. In the second part of the song the metre changes to common time and the marking is *Tempo marcia misterioso*. This means 'at a march-like speed and mysteriously'. The repeated octaves in the left hand of the piano set up the marching feel and suggest the sexton getting out of bed and heading off to investigate the mystery. Try to sing very quietly here but notice that there is a gradual *crescendo* as the sexton sets out. The following slower section also needs to be sung quietly but very deliberately, interrupted by the loud piano chords. The return to $\frac{6}{8}$ brings back the sounds of the bells and the ending should be really quiet and rather spooky as your listener is left wondering about the possibility of ghosts in the belfry.

This song is very much a duet between the singer and the accompaniment as the piano part contains effects that help establish the atmosphere of the piece. How can you use your voice to create different moods and effects? You could try experimenting with ways to colour your sounds to achieve all sorts of different moods.

Mervyn Burtch was a 20th-century Welsh composer who was especially noted for his compositions for young musicians including a number of operas written for performance by children.

The words of this song at first may seem a little strange. Chelsea is a district in London and the coach and six is an old-fashioned carriage pulled by six horses. Along with this coach 'all the world' is trying to reach the 'World's End', a refrain that keeps being repeated. Reaching the World's End is perhaps an odd thing to want but, in this song, the World's End is in fact a part of Chelsea. King James II, in the 17th century, used to ride down the King's Road in Chelsea and talk about it being the end of the world. So, everyone in this song is not worried about the potential destruction of the earth but instead wanting to be in the centre of London!

There is a lively feel to the song and it needs to be sung with a real 'spring in its step' to portray all the huge number of different people moving towards the World's End. There are some interesting changes of key throughout the song with lots of accidentals either flattening or sharpening notes. So be very careful that all the notes are sung well in tune. Try practising each phrase slowly at first to make sure that you are singing right through the centre of every note.

In order to add lots of character to your singing, you need to know what sort of people the song is about. Some of them may have unfamiliar roles so see what you can find out about what an Alderman or a Chamberlain did for example.

Clifford Crawley was born in England and gained a Fellowship from Trinity College London after studies at Durham University. In later life he moved to Canada where he continued to compose right up until his death in 2016.

In this song, Clifford Crawley has written both the words and the music. There are two very distinct parts to the song with the first describing Abdul and his magic act and the second asking the question about where he learnt his conjuring tricks. The minor key sets up a slightly spooky mood in the first part and you need to convey this atmosphere, portraying the character of Abdul to your listeners. Take care with the descending octave interval right at the opening and make sure that consonants, particularly those at the ends of words, are very clear. Think carefully about how long to make the two pauses at the end of this section. You need to show that there is a definite change of mood coming as the music moves from the $\frac{6}{8}$ metre into $\frac{2}{4}$. Keep the *staccato* on the words: 'they don't teach things like that in school' really light and well articulated. At the very end of the song make sure you get back into the $\frac{6}{8}$ feel and think about how many times you want to repeat the 'and you' bars. You could imagine that you have a whole audience of people listening to you, and you are pointing at them one by one as you sing. You may not want to repeat the bar too many times though!

There is a sense in this song that there is no such thing as magic and that magicians simply 'fool' people with their tricks. Have you ever learnt a 'magic' trick? You could try watching a recording of a magician and see if you can work out how it was done.

This song is not at all what it seems as it is about a witch who wishes she were human. So even though, in the first verse, she has everything a witch should have with a black cat and a pointed hat, she casts a spell to transform herself into an ordinary person with a white cat and a feathered hat instead. This means you need to make sure that you really communicate the story to your listeners. This can be achieved using all the different changes of tempo throughout the song. At the very beginning the music is marked *Adagio*, which means slow but by the time you come in, the tempo is *Allegro* which means fast. So sing with plenty of spirit but don't rush. As the spell is cast in the closing bars there is a big change of tempo back into *Adagio*. Think about the change of speed you would like to make, also noticing that, as you cast the spell, you need to get gradually faster to observe the marking of *poco a poco accel.* Try experimenting with different speeds in your practice until you find ones that you feel comfortable with.

The character of Grizelda changes completely in this song. Can you think of other characters in stories or poems you have read who change? Perhaps you could write your own words about someone who transforms in some way.

Judith Exley is from New Zealand and she has always been fascinated by music from Japan and Indonesia, with an especial fondness for the Gamelan and its repertoire.

This song is short but quite complex. This is because the accompaniment is quite sparse and so does not give much support to the singer. Pitching notes is therefore very important and you need to use your 'inner' voice to 'hear' the notes before you come in. Make sure too that you stay completely in tune as you sing the unaccompanied phrases at the beginning. There are some 'effects' that need careful thought. So, for example: keep the triplet *staccato* on the word 'prejudiced' particularly neat and crisp and really practise the slow slide down on the word 'peacock' to ensure that it is even and that it starts and finishes on the right note. Think about how you can express suitable 'disgust' on the high note on 'face' and how expressive you can make the word 'breathes' using a breathy tone. There is an interesting piano interlude between the two parts of this song so remember to stay focussed and committed even though you are not actually singing.

The composer has written the words: 'With a sense of distaste' at the beginning and there is a definite feeling that a fly is not a very popular creature! Are there animals that you don't like? Try to think how they make you feel as you sing.

Skempton   Pigs Could Fly   page 34

Howard Skempton is an award-winning composer, composition teacher, accordionist and music publisher. His compositional roots are in the experimental tradition and his music often has a feeling of immediacy and directness.

The words of this song are written by the composer and the whole certainly has an immediate impact with its eccentric view of the flying pig with 'real flair' being superior to all other animals. It needs to be sung with lots of energy and breathing needs to be quick and efficient as there is very little time to stop and think! Keep your tone light and even and don't be tempted to push the sound at all. The consecutive $\frac{3}{4}$ then $\frac{2}{4}$ bars almost give the song a sense of being in an irregular metre but if you concentrate on keeping a very strong sense of a continuous beat you will find that the whole slots into place. Try practising clapping or stamping the pulse while you say the words out loud in time. There are numerous repetitions of melodic motifs in the song, especially the rising interval of a fifth, but make sure that each one is pitched accurately as the words change. Make sure that your tongue is very flexible and free as you sing the final section of the song.

This song has been sung by a number of choirs. How difficult do you think it would be to keep everyone together? You could try singing this as a unison song with friends and see if you can stay in time with each other. Do you think that it works best as a solo song or as a choir piece?

Telfer   On the Back of an Eagle   page 36

Nancy Telfer is a Canadian composer with over 350 works to her name. She believes in capturing the power of the imagination in her compositions and is drawn to take inspiration from the beauty of the natural environment.

This song certainly takes the singer on a journey through the natural and the imagined world with the thought of flying in the clear blue sky on the back of a magnificent bird of prey, the eagle. You need to feel a sense of space and freedom when you sing this song, allowing each phrase to have a natural shape of rising and falling. Longer notes need to be carefully sustained and not cut short or this will leave gaps in the music and spoil the flow of the lines. There is not much contrast in the dynamics but do try to feel a difference between the *mf* sections and the *f* sections. Even in the loudest passages, your sound should never be over strong. Don't allow yourself to get tense or feel you are having to make sound but keep the throat open and the shoulders loose to allow you to sing with a warm and naturally resonant quality.

The nearest any of us can get to flying is hang-gliding but can you imagine what it would be like to be able to fly completely on our own? Think about all the sights you would see and how different things would look from above. Try writing some descriptions of everything or even making up a story in which you could fly.

Vine   Love Me Sweet   page 40

Carl Vine is an Australian composer. After studying physics and then music at the University of Western Australia he became a freelance pianist and composer. In 2005 he received the Don Banks Award for Outstanding Contribution to Australian Music and in 2014 he was appointed senior lecturer in composition at the Sydney Conservatorium of Music.

This song is a voice and piano version of the music that was originally the theme tune to a TV series called *The Battlers*. The text is adapted from the poem 'A Man's Requirements' by Elizabeth Barrett Browning (1806-1861). It is a tender, lyrical love song moving mostly in steps with no large leaps to disturb the *legato*. The phrases need to be sung very evenly with the breath pressure firmly underpinning each one, as the note values throughout the song are mostly long. There is plenty of time to breathe at the ends of phrases so make sure that you always breathe deeply into the body. Feel where each line is travelling to so that every note you sing is nourished. The $\frac{3}{4}$ metre gives the whole a gentle lilt so don't allow this song to drag.

In the original version instruments were used rather than just the piano. Can you find a recording of this version and see if you can identify which instruments are playing? What difference does using these instruments make to the feel of the song?

Coghlan & Coghlan Rocking in Rhythm   page 44

This contemporary song by Mira and Michael Coghlan celebrates the joys of singing using a catchy, jazzy feel with an easy swing lilt.

You need to feel the swing in this song moving from straight rhythm to swung rhythm so that notes are not sung equally. Feel the 'bounce' in the syncopation on words like 'singing' and 'snapping' and think about how you will negotiate the triplets on 'singing and feeling just fine'. There are some semitones, which need to be pitched very carefully so really feel the difference between the flats and the naturals in the *coda* section of the song. Make sure that you have plenty of energy left for the end, which finishes with a real flourish and a big *crescendo* up to *ff*. Don't forget that the very final word is whispered. Stay really confident and project this with a 'stage whisper' so that it can still be heard.

This is a great song to sing with friends. You could try singing it together or take it in turns to sing phrases or even add some notes of your own, perhaps in the rests. There could even be opportunities for some instrumental work, perhaps with percussion instruments.

Hamilton   Chocolate (from *Just Desserts*)   page 47

David Hamilton is from New Zealand. He is a composer and conductor with a keen interest in choral music and his works have been performed in countries across the world. 'Chocolate' comes from a collection of songs for young singers about food called *Just Desserts* written in 1999.

The opening to this song has a Latin dance feel with its cross rhythms and upbeat tempo. This sets up a cheerful mood and you need to sing this song with real enthusiasm. Keep the syncopation absolutely tight as you pick up the beat and stay very connected with what is happening in the piano accompaniment. Use strong clear words to help give your singing drive and momentum and make sure that you finish with a bright confident *ff* and crisp accents. The way to achieve really firm accents is to almost 'bite' into the consonants to give the required percussive feel. This will help to get across the rather odd idea of 'choc'late flavoured toothpaste'!

It is almost impossible to keep still when listening to Latin dance music. See if you can find a recording of a Samba for example to experience the energy and spirit of the music. You may also be able to watch people dancing to this sort of music. It looks complicated but anyone can join in so why don't you have a go at trying out some Latin moves?